Ready to Learn

ALPHABET &
BEGINNING
SOUNDS

by Imogene Forte

Incentive Publications, Inc.
Nashville, Tennessee

Illustrated by Gayle Harvey
Cover by Geoffrey Brittingham
Edited by Charlotte Bosarge

ISBN 0-86530-597-8

1   2   3   4   5   6   7   8   9   10   07   06   05   04

PRINTED IN THE UNITED STATES OF AMERICA
www.incentivepublications.com

Table of Contents

To Parents and Teachers

Why You Need This Book

- The Ready to Learn books capitalize on the vitally important "teachable" years from 4 to 6.
- Basic skills and concepts are introduced to help pave the way to increased self-confidence and reinforced lifelong learning success.

What Children Will Learn From This Book

- Children will learn the following basic alphabet and beginning sounds skills and concepts which are so important to early learning success:

    o *Discriminating Visually*

    o *Recognizing Capital Letters A-Z*

    o *Recognizing Lowercase Letters A-Z*

    o *Recognizing and Matching Upper with Lowercase Letters*

    o *Recognizing Beginning Sound Making Pictures and Words*

    o *Associating Words and Pictures*

    o *Recognizing Alphabetical Sequence*

    o *Following Directions*

How to Get the Most From This Book

- Read and interpret the directions for the child.
- Maintain a light and relaxed atmosphere.
- Allow the child to work at his or her own pace, free from pressure to perform.
- Praise the child's efforts!

Skills Checklist

Alphabet & Beginning Sounds

Capital Letters

It is ABC day at the zoo.
Paula Parrot is in charge of all the letters
from A to Z.
Trace and say the capital letters from A to Z.

Recognizing Capital Letters A to Z

*Ready To Learn Series — **Alphabet & Beginning Sound***
Copyright ©2003 by Incentive Publications, Inc., Nashville, TN

Lowercase Letters

The lowercase letters are ready for
ABC day at the zoo, too.
Trace and say the lowercase letters
from A to Z.

a b c d e f g

h i j k l m n

o p q r s t u

v w x y z

A

Ally Alligator is swimming with the capital A.
Circle the matching lowercase letter.

c   g   a   e

 Recognizing and Matching Capital and Lowercase Letters (A a)

*Ready To Learn Series — **Alphabet & Beginning Sound***
Copyright ©2003 by Incentive Publications, Inc., Nashville, TN

A

Ally alligator has an apple, an orange, an apricot, a banana, and an avocado.

Color the pictures of three fruits whose names begin with **A**.

B

Benny Bear brought the capital B.
Circle the matching lowercase letter.

d P b s

Recognizing and Matching Capital and Lowercase Letters (B-b)

*Ready To Learn Series — **Alphabet & Beginning Sound***
Copyright ©2003 by Incentive Publications, Inc., Nashville, TN

B

Benny Bear loves to play with his ball, bat, car, truck, and bike.

Make an X on the toys whose names begin with **B**.

C

Cora Camel cares for the capital C.
Circle the matching lowercase letter.

e a o c

*Ready To Learn Series — **Alphabet & Beginning Soun***
Copyright ©2003 by Incentive Publications, Inc., Nashville, T

C

Cora Camel carries her comb, brush, cap, cup, and shoes in a special carrying case.

Color the pictures of three things whose names being with **C**.

D

Dancing Dan Dog is dancing around the capital D.

Circle the matching lowercase letter.

e g b d

Recognizing and Matching Capital and Lowercase Letters (D-d)

*Ready To Learn Series — **Alphabet & Beginning Soun***

D

☆ Dancing Dan Dog dances with his friends the deer, the bear, the duck, and the donkey.

Make a box around the pictures of four animals whose names begin with **D**.

E

Ellie Elephant is giving the capital E a ride.

Circle the matching lowercase letter.

g   e   c   u

Recognizing and Matching Capital and Lowercase Letters (E-e)

*Ready To Learn Series — **Alphabet & Beginning Soun***

E

Ellie Elephant paints pictures of an eagle, an egg, a parrot, an eel, and an owl.

Color the pictures of three things whose names begin with **E**.

F

Fanci Frog has finally found the capital F.
Make an X on all the letters except the matching
lowercase letter.

t f e s

Recognizing and Matching Capital and Lowercase Letters (F-f)

Ready To Learn Series — Alphabet & Beginning Sound
Copyright ©2003 by Incentive Publications, Inc., Nashville, T

F

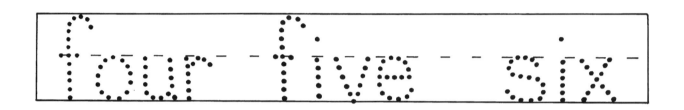

Fanci Frog can write
the numbers four, five, six,
seven and fifteen.

Circle three numbers whose names begin with **F**.

four five six

seven fifteen

G

Grumpy Gus Giraffe is guarding the capital G.

Circle the matching lowercase letter.

g e u d

Recognizing and Matching Capital and Lowercase Letters (G-g)

Ready To Learn Series — *Alphabet & Beginning Sound*

G

Grumpy Gus Giraffe stretches his neck to see a goat, a goose, a snail, a gull, and a parrot.

Color the pictures of three animals whose names begin with **G**.

H

Hallie Hippo is holding the capital H close to her heart.
Make a box around the matching lowercase letter.

m   n   h   e

H

Hallie Hippo combs her hair, shakes her hips, waves her hand, and winks her eye.

Color the pictures of three body parts whose names begin with **H**.

I

Inga Insect is ignoring the capital I.

Make an X on all the letters except the matching lowercase letter.

I e i t

Recognizing and Matching Capital and Lowercase Letters (I-i)

*Ready To Learn Series — **Alphabet & Beginning Sound***
Copyright ©2003 by Incentive Publications, Inc., Nashville, T

I

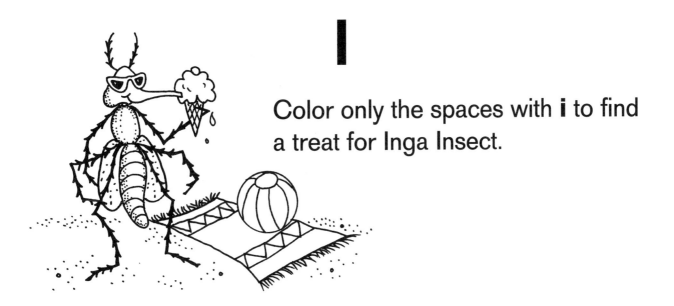

Color only the spaces with **i** to find a treat for Inga Insect.

J

Jenni Jellyfish is jumping rope with the capital J.

Circle the matching lowercase letter.

t   p   j   g

Recognizing and Matching Capital and Lowercase Letters (J-j)

*Ready To Learn Series — **Alphabet & Beginning Sound***

J

Jenni Jellyfish jumps rope with her friends Joey, Fanci, Jan, Julie, and Paula.

Color the hats of the friends whose names begin with the same letter as the name **Jenni**.

K

Katie Kangaroo keeps the capital **K** in her pouch.
Make an X on all the lowercase letters
except the matching one.

j   k   z   m   t

*Recognizing and Matching Capital
and Lowercase Letters (K-k)*

Ready To Learn Series — Alphabet & Beginning Soun
Copyright ©2003 by Incentive Publications, Inc., Nashville, T

K

Draw dot to dot from A to K and you will find
a friend for Katie Kangaroo.

L

Luke the Lion loves the capital L.

Circle the matching lowercase letter.

l   r   t   b

*Ready To Learn Series — **Alphabet & Beginning Sound***

L

Help Luke the lion get to his den.
Make an X on the pictures of animals whose names
do not begin with **L**.

LUKE
LION

M

Monty Monkey may be small but he makes the capital M mighty.

Circle the matching lowercase letter.

d   m   n   r

M

Monty Monkey invited Molly, Robbie, Mary, and Milt to his party.

Color the hats of the monkeys who names begin with **M**.

N

Nettie Nightingale sings lovely songs to the capital N.

Circle the matching lowercase letter.

m   n   g   v

*Ready To Learn Series — **Alphabet & Beginning Soun***
Copyright ©2003 by Incentive Publications, Inc., Nashville, T

N

Nancy, Nick, Paula, Ned and Noel sing in the choir with Nettie Nightingale.

Make an X on the picture of the bird whose name does not begin with the same letter as Nellie's.

O

Ollie Owl opens doors for the capital O.

Circle the matching lowercase letter.

c   e   o   g

*Recognizing and Matching Capital
and Lowercase Letters (O-o)*

Ready To Learn Series — Alphabet & Beginning Sound

O

Follow the dots from a to o to find a picture
of Ollie Owl flying over the barn.

P

The capital P is proudly parading past Paula Parrot.

Make a box around the matching lowercase letter.

a   q   p   u

JUDGES' BOOTH

PLEASANTVILLE'S ST. PATRICK'S DAY PARADE

P

Paula Parrot picks the panda, the owl, the penguin, and the pony for her team.

Color the pictures of the animals whose names begin with **P**.

Q

Quincy Quail is quietly watching over the capital Q.

Circle the matching lowercase letter.

q   o   c   p

Q

Quincy Quail wants to make a quilt from letter blocks.
Color the blocks red that start with the same letter as
Quincy Quail's name.

R

Robbie Raccoon rescues the capital R from a dip in the river.

Circle the matching lowercase letter.

n   m   r   w

R

Find and color the 5 capital R's that Robbie Raccoon has hidden in the forest.

Can you circle and name all the other letters?

S

Slowly, Snippy Snail slides toward the capital S.

Circle the matching lowercase letter.

y   e   s   r

*Ready To Learn Series — **Alphabet & Beginning Soun***

S

Snippy Snail sails smooth seas under sunny skies in a sailboat built for three.

Color Snippy Snail brown. | Color the smooth sea blue.
Color the sailboat green. | Color the sun yellow.

T

The capital T is taking a trip on Tommy Turtle's tail.

Draw a box around the matching lowercase letter.

l   i   t   u

TASMANIA

Timbuktu

TAHITA

Ready To Learn Series — *Alphabet & Beginning Sound*
Copyright ©2003 by Incentive Publications, Inc., Nashville, T'

T

Tommy Turtle and his friends are lining up for the big turtle race.

Color the pictures of the racers whose names begin with the same letter as the word **turtle**.

U

Ulie Unicorn waits under the umbrella for the capital U.
Circle the matching lowercase letter.

v   y   u   c

U

Help Ulie Unicorn match animals' names with beginning sounds.

Draw lines to match each letter with an animal whose name has the same beginning sound.

Aa

Ee

Ii

Oo

V

Mr. Van Voss the zookeeper wears the capital V on his vest.
Circle the matching lowercase letter.

u   v   c   w

V

Mr. Van Voss checks the letters very carefully every night.

Trace and say the name of each letter.
Color the **V** red.

W

The capital W is welcomed to the zoo by Word Bird.

Circle the matching lowercase letter.

u   v   w   c

W

Word Bird watches Wally, Willie, Tommy, and Wanda write their names.

Color the pictures of friends who names begin with the same letter as Word Bird's name.

X

X marks the spot where the animal trainer waits with the capital X.

Circle the matching lowercase letter.

k   w   z   x

ABC Order

The animal trainer works extra hard to keep his list exactly right.

Find letters on the ABC chart to fill in his list.

Y

Yannie Yak yawns while waiting for the capital Y to wake up.

Circle the matching lowercase letter.

g   p   y   q

*Ready To Learn Series — **Alphabet & Beginning Sound***
Copyright ©2003 by Incentive Publications, Inc., Nashville, TN

Z

Zelda Zebra is last in line with the capital Z.

Circle the matching lowercase letter.

f   t   z   e

All Aboard

The Zoo train is ready to roll!
Help Paula Parrot check her list.

Say the letters from A to Z
to make your way from
Allie Alligator to Zelda Zebra.

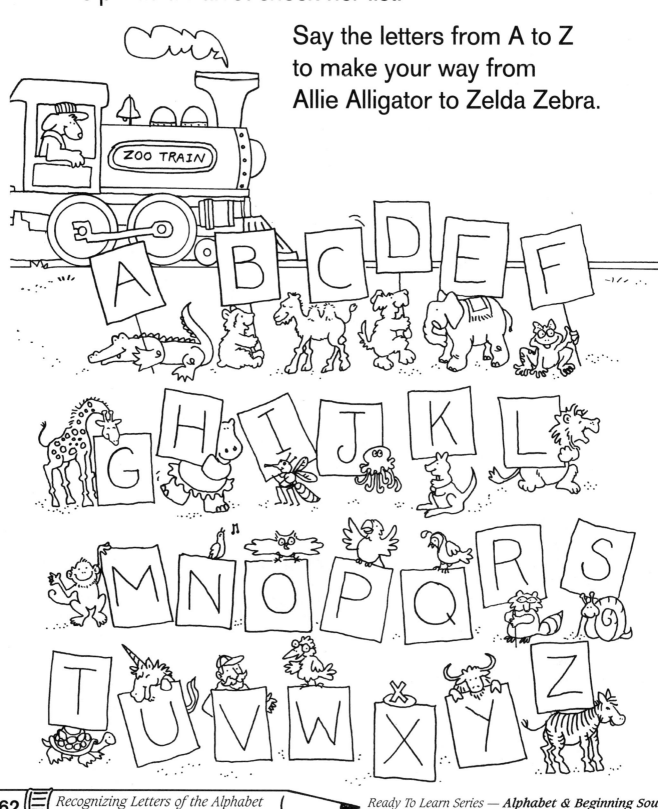

*Ready To Learn Series — **Alphabet & Beginning Sound***
Copyright ©2003 by Incentive Publications, Inc., Nashville, T

More Things to Do

Activities and Projects to Help Young Children Learn about the Alphabet & Beginning Sounds

- On 3 x 5 index cards, print the letters of the alphabet. Use both capital and lowercase letters. Cut pictures from magazines of objects beginning with each letter of the alphabet. Help the child match the letter cards and picture cards.

- Place five of the letter cards on the floor. Have the child cover both eyes. Remove a card. Let the child guess which one is missing. Repeat the process, removing a different card each time. Gradually increase the number of cards to increase perceptual skills, as well as reinforce letter recognition skills.

- On 3 x 5 index cards, print the names of common household objects. Trace in bold and underline the first letter of the word (for example, **table**). Then, attach each card at the child's eye level with masking tape to the appropriate object. Then, remove from the objects and put them in a stack easily accessible to the child. Ask the child to replace each card to the correct object.

- Use the letter cards to teach alphabetical sequence. Place the cards on the floor in random order and ask the child to arrange them sequentially. Less mature children may need to begin with part of the letters in place and being asked to "fill in the gaps" and work up gradually to constructing the entire sequence from A to Z.

- Give the child several old magazines and/or catalogs. Ask the child to find and circle with a crayon, marker, or pencil both capital and lowercase letters.

- Play an ABC version of "I Spy" with the child. Take turns spotting objects that begin with each letter of the alphabet A through Z!

- When playing hide and seek, encourage the seeker to sing the alphabet song, instead of counting to 10, while the hiders are hiding.

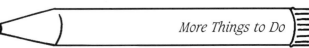